COLOR ME STRONGER

This book belongs to:

Color and Activity

Best for Ages 3+
Develops coloring skills
Encourages concentration
Highlights Making Fitness Fun
Promotes Artistic expression
#colormestronger

© Color Me Stronger

Draw Yourself Working Out

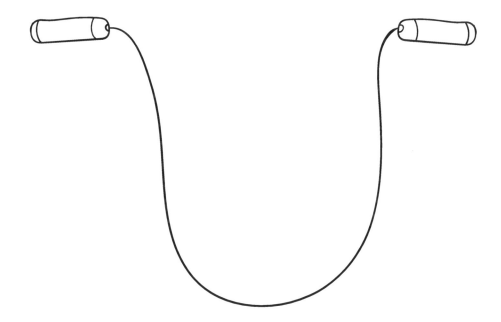

Draw Yourself Working Out

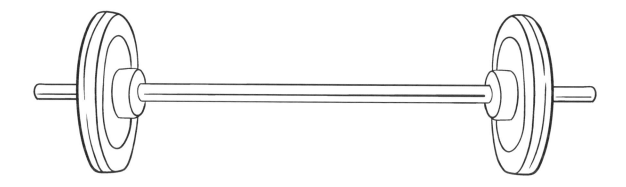

Draw Yourself Working Out

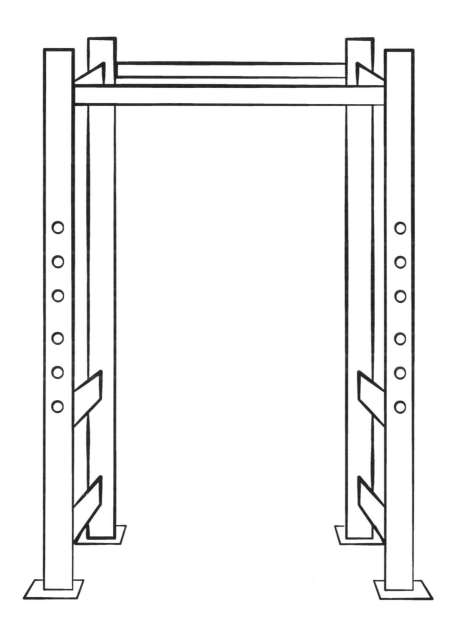

Help her get to her Barbell

Help him get to his Barbell

1- Pink

2- Purple

3- Blue

4- Green

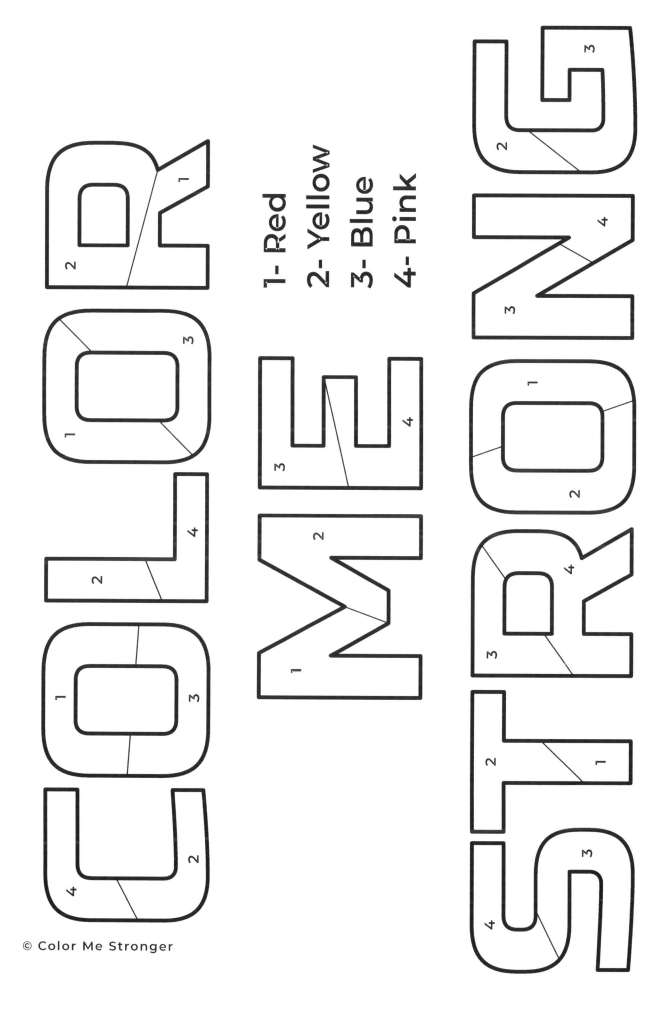

1- Red
2- Yellow
3- Blue
4- Pink

Made in United States
Troutdale, OR
07/29/2024